GW00579251

Published 2004
© International Music Publications
Music arranged and engraved by Artemis Music Ltd
Design by Form® www.form.uk.com
Photography by Ellis Parrinder

What I Go To School For

Her voice is echoed in my mind
I count the days 'til she is mine.
Can't tell my friends 'cos they will laugh
I love a member of the staff.

I fight my way to front of class
To get the best view of her ass.
I drop a pencil on the floor
She bends down and shows me more...

Chorus
That's what I go to school for
Even though it is a real bore
You can call me crazy
I know that she craves me.
That's what I go to school for
Even though it is a real bore
Girlfriends I've had plenty
None like Miss Mackenzie
That's what I go to school for
That's what I go to school for.

So she may be thirty three
But that doesn't bother me.
Her boyfriend's working out of town
I find a reason to go round.

I climb a tree outside her home
To make sure that she's alone.
I see her in her underwear
I can't help but stop and stare...

Chorus

Everyone that you teach all day
Knows you're looking at me in a different way.
I guess that's why
My marks are getting so high.
I could see those tell tale signs
Telling me that I was on your mind.
I could see that you wanted more
When you told me that
I'm what you go to school for
I'm what you go to school for

She's packed her bag it's in the trunk.
Looks like she picked herself her hunk.
We drive past school to say goodbye
My friends they can't believe their eyes.

Chorus

You Said No (Crash And Burn)

You're so fit and you know it
And I only dream of you
'Cos my life's such a bitch
But you can change it

Maybe you need somebody just like me,
Don't turn me down 'cos I've got no car and I've got
No money...

Chorus
I asked you to dance at the disco
But you said No!
The whole world was watching and laughing
On the day that I crashed and burned...
At your feet!

Since the day you dissed me
I'm feeling so pathetic,
'Cos the guys... well they've ditched me
And it's all because of...

You and your friends are laughing at me now
You think that I'm nothing
Ask your sister what you're missing!

Chorus

Maybe you think that you're too good for me
Tonight when you get home you're gonna see that
I know, I've got something better than you baby

Chorus

Britney

Your face is everywhere I go now
And you're on every television show now,
Baby I need you.
You're everything I want in someone,
But you don't even know who I am,
Baby why should you?

Sweating all over your video,
Watching every single scene in slow mo.
Trackin you down on the Internet
Cos I ain't seen you naked yet...

Chorus
I want you Britney,
I need you here with me.
You know that I won't stop until I've got you.
I want you Britney.

I even know the place that you live,
And I don't care who your boyfriend is,
Cos one day it's gonna be me.
And I think that I'm obsessed with you girl,
Cos I copy everything you do now,
And Pepsi lets me taste you,

God must have spent a little more time on you,
In school uniform you look so good.
And you say that you're not a girl,
I'll make you a woman.

Chorus

Every single thing you do,
Every time I look at you,
I become a slave for you,
You drive me crazy.
You know that I won't stop until I've got you.
I want you Britney.

What the hell can I do,
To get closer to you.
You can run you can't hide,
I'll make you feel good inside.
What the hell can I do,
To get closer to you.
You can run you can't hide,
I'll make you feel good inside...

Chorus

Losing You

Sitting here alone thinking it through,
Trying to convince myself that I'm not losing you.
Why can't you just forget the things I said?
I was angry at the time but now I've cleared my head.
It was so strong, where did it all go wrong?

Chorus
So tell me why I'm swimming against the tide?
And I'm praying for a lifeline, 'cause I'm losing you.
So tell me why you don't care enough to try?
Are you giving up this fight?
I can't stand, won't stand losing you.

You don't have to say a word, it's in your eyes,
What can I do to convince you that we need more time?
And I know I may have made a few mistakes,
But losing you is just too much for me to take.
It was so strong, where did it all go wrong?

Chorus

So tell me what to say because I need a chance to change,
And I won't let you walk away.

Chorus

And I'm praying for a lifeline, 'cause I'm losing you.
So tell me why you don't care enough to try?
Are you giving up this fight?
I can't stand, won't stand losing you,
Won't stand losing you, won't stand losing you.

Year 3000

One day when I came home at lunchtime
I heard a funny noise
Went out to the back yard to find out if it was
one of those rowdy boys.
Stood there was my neighbour called Peter
and a Flux Capacitor

He told me he built a time machine
Like the one in the film I've seen
Yeah yeah... He said...

Chorus
I've been to the year three thousand,
Not much has changed but they lived under water,
And your Great great great grand daughter,
Is pretty fine (Is pretty fine)

He took me to the future in the flux thing and I saw everything
Boybands and another one and another one... and another one!
Triple breasted women swim around town... totally naked!

We drove around in the time machine
Like the one in the film I've seen...
Yeah yeah... He said...

Chorus

I took a trip to the year three thousand
This song had gone multi platinum
Everybody bought our seventh album
It had outsold Michael Jackson
I took a trip to the year three thousand
This song had gone multi platinum
Everybody bought our seventh album, seventh album

He told me he built a time machine
Like the one in the film I've seen
Yeah yeah... He said...

Chorus

Psycho Girl

She's so weird it scares me,
I don't think she likes me.
And thinking of her name
Is driving me insane.

Chorus
She's my psycho girl
My psycho girlfriend,
Everything I say,
She takes it the wrong way.
She's my psycho girl
A living nightmare,
She's everything I need,
But I can't stand her.

I cant change her thinking,
But she's so good looking,
And thinking of her name
It's driving me insane...

Chorus

We spent the night in,
We started fighting,
Since then it's never been the same.

Thinking of her name,
Is driving me insane...

Chorus

All The Way

It happens every time,
You've given me the sign,
We start to get it on,
But then you stop me.
You know I've had it up to here,
You need to be more clear,
Cos you're the one that let me here,
So take me.

Chorus
Cos you said that you would,
But then you changed your mind,
How could you do this to me,
It's just so unkind.
And it's cruel if you say that you'll go all the way,
I can't wait for the day,
That you don't change your mind,

You've got to understand,
Things are getting out of hand,
You can't just leave me sitting here unseen to.
You know I don't know what to do,
Or how long to wait for you,
You said you needed time so I wont rush you.

Chorus

I'll never let you down,
I'll always be around,
When you need someone
To catch you when you fall down.
I'm waiting here for you,
If you decide you want to.
If you want me to stay
Then I'm only a phone call away.

Chorus

Sleeping With The Light On

Along she came with her picture,
Put it in a frame so I won't miss her.
Got on a plane from London Heathrow,
It seems such a shame, yeah.

Chorus
I feel her slipping through my fingers,
Now she's gone I'm sleeping with the light on.
And shocks went through my veins,
Now that she's gone I'm sleeping with the light on.

Heard she's engaged, spoke to her best friend,
No-one's to blame, here's where it all ends.
And I feel the pain 'cause I'm without her,
I feel the pain, yeah.

Chorus

I see the sight with a different light,
Words cannot describe the way I'm feeling.
'Cause I've been searching in my head
For the words I thought she said for too long.

Chorus

Dawson's Geek

You think you know it all,
I see it in the way you're speaking.
The long words that you use,
Are starting to get irritating.
I've got the urge to knock you out,
And I can't handle this.
The ladder by your bedroom window
Really takes the piss.

Step back take a look at where you're at,
You're just a raving Dawson's maniac...

Chorus
You think that you know everything,
Take one step back and look at yourself.
I think you don't know anything,
All my friends think that you're such a freak,
And you're just a Dawson's geek,
Dawson's Dawson's geek.

Why can't you see that you don't look like him
in any way,
At least that kid has friends and that's a lot more
Than you can say.
You've lost your mind and I don't think that you
Know who you are.
Naming you dog 'Pacey' was taking things a little
too far.

Step back take a look at where you're at,
You're just a raving Dawson's maniac...

Chorus

I guess I'll have to wait for your life to be over,
I guess I'll have to wait,
I guess I'll have to wait...

Oi! Oi!

I think you don't know anything,
All my friends think that you're such a freak,
And you're just a Dawson's geek,

Chorus

Everything I Knew

Everything I knew, it just went out the window.
Now I can't depend on you forever.
And I never thought I'd see my life walk away from me,
I thought we'd always be together.

No, I shouldn't have to pay for every word I say,
And I wish I could change your decision.
Now you know that I've tried to tell you what it's like,
But you just wouldn't listen.

Chorus
Let's go back, let's rewind to the days
That remind me of all the good times that we spent together.
And I don't know why we just let it all slide,
When we both knew inside we were right for each other.

I don't know what to do,
'Cause you're everything that I knew.

Every day's the same, it's like tomorrow never came.
We used to talk about whatever.
And the seasons never changed, we never used to act our age,
Every time we were together.

No, I shouldn't have to pay for every word I say,
And I wish I could change your decision.
Now you know that I've tried to tell you what it's like,
But you just wouldn't listen.

Chorus

I don't know what to do,
'Cause you're everything that I knew.

How can you just walk out of my life
Without even giving a reason?
And how can you look so good
The day I watched you leave me?

Chorus

Oh, yeah yeah.

When Day Turns Into Night

Nobody's there when you get home,
You're renting movies on your own,
My photo's on your bedroom wall,
You sit there waiting for my call.

Chorus
And I know I leave you on your own,
And I need you to be strong when I'm walking away.
And I hate to say goodbye,
It gets harder every time.
What I feel you feel inside,
When the day turns into night.

Another tired afternoon,
Another dusty motel room,
I hate the fact that you're not here,
But now I'm counting down the days till I get there.

Chorus

Without You

The way you always made me look at you
With all the simple things you said,
The way so many things surrounded you
And all the tears it seemed to make.

And now I'm falling, there's nothing left to say.
And I can't break free, not from in me there.

Chorus
I can't breathe without you, I can't breathe without you,
I can't breathe without you, without you, without you, without you.

The way I thought I'd never leave this place,
The way you made it seem so real,
'Cause you had faith and you had empathy
And all I needed was this.

And now I'm falling, I've got nothing left to say.
And I can't break free, not from in me there.

How can I let you leave this way?
Without you I'm not at all.
And I see things now, all those memories
Just to see you again.

Loser Kid

I was always picked last for teams,
I wore my sister's jeans,
I was a loser kid.
And the teachers didn't care,
They just left me sitting there,
I don't know what I did
But since then,
How the tides have turned,

Chorus
Cos I used to be the loser kid,
Who always ran away and hid.
No one took the time to know me,
The kick me sign was always on me.
Now everybody wants to know,
What I do and where I go,
At least I know they wont forget me,
Cos I live with Miss Mackenzie.

And now it's all history,
And I put it all behind me,
Look at what I've become.
I get recognized in the street,
And everyone I meet,
Remembers the news I made.
But since then,
How the tides have turned,

Chorus

When I see the way you look at me,
It takes me back to how it used to be.
And still it's clear,
The way you locked the class room door,
And whispered in my ear..
'Your what I go to school for,
You are,
The one I go to school for.'

Chorus

What I Go To School For

Words and Music by James Bourne, Mathew Sargeant,
Charlie Simpson, John McLaughlin and Steve Robson

Verse 3:
She's packed her bag, it's in the trunk
Looks like she's picked herself a hunk
We drive by school to say goodbye
My friends, they can't believe their eyes.

That's what I go to school for *etc.*

You Said No
(Crash And Burn)

Words and Music by James Bourne, Mathew Sargeant, Charlie Simpson, John McLaughlin and Steve Robson

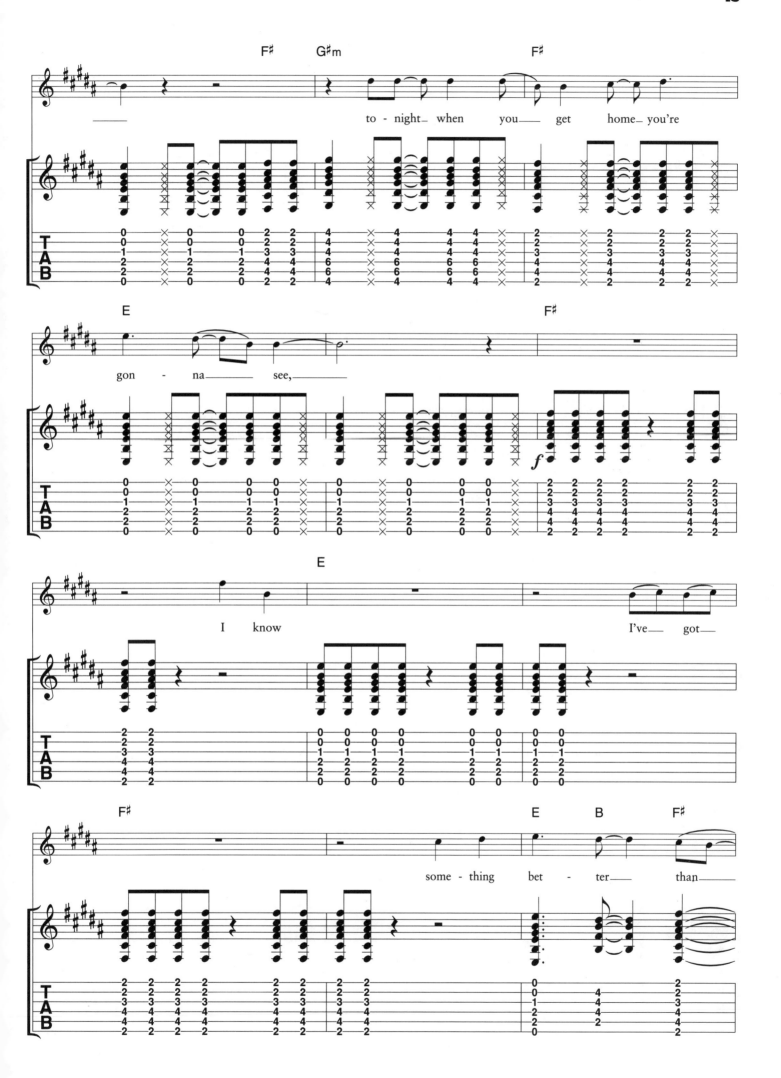

Britney

Words and Music by James Bourne, John McLaughlin and Steve Robson

Losing You

Words and Music by James Bourne, Mathew Sargeant, Charlie Simpson, John McLaughlin and Steve Robson

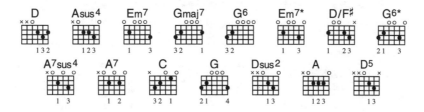

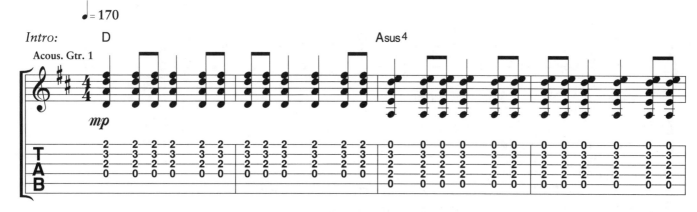

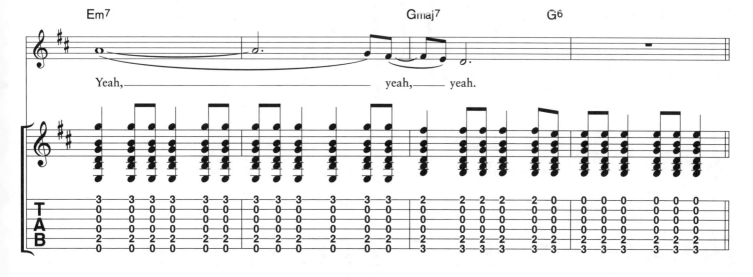

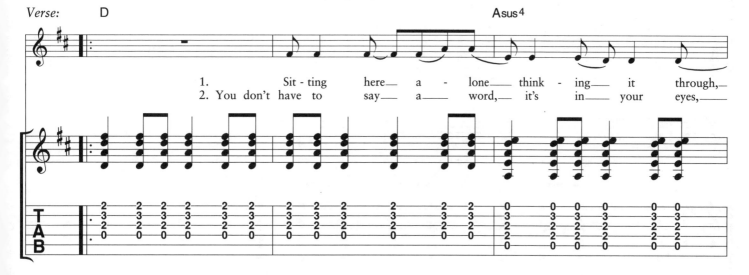

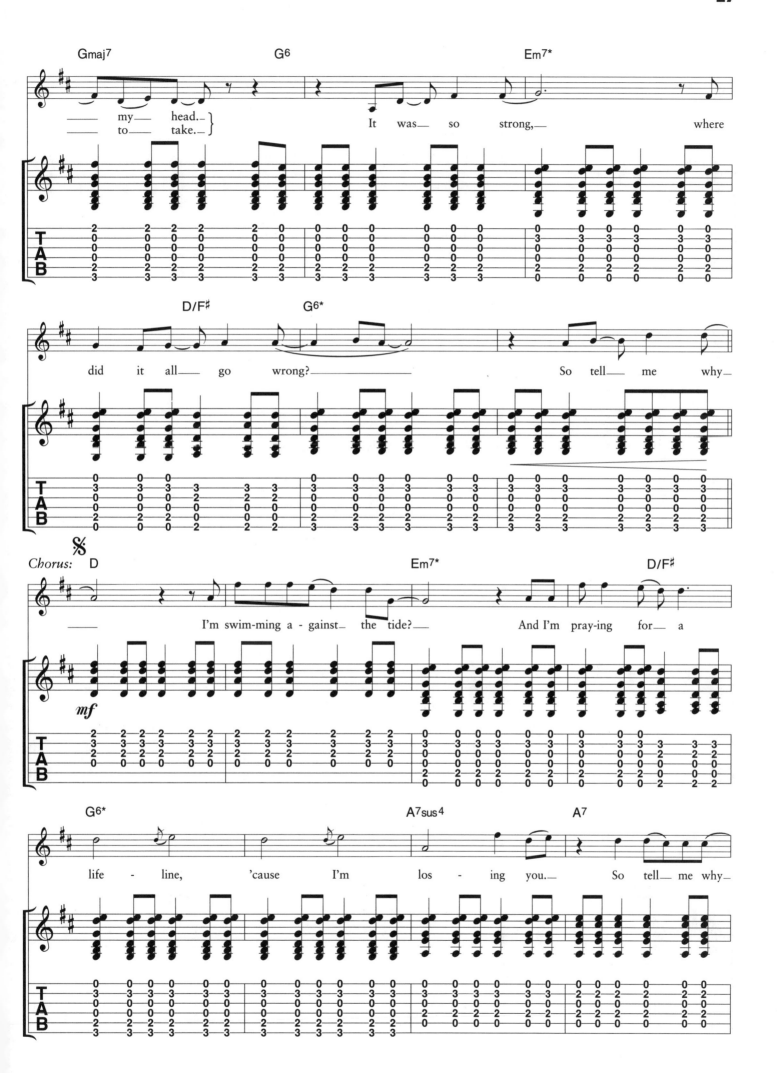

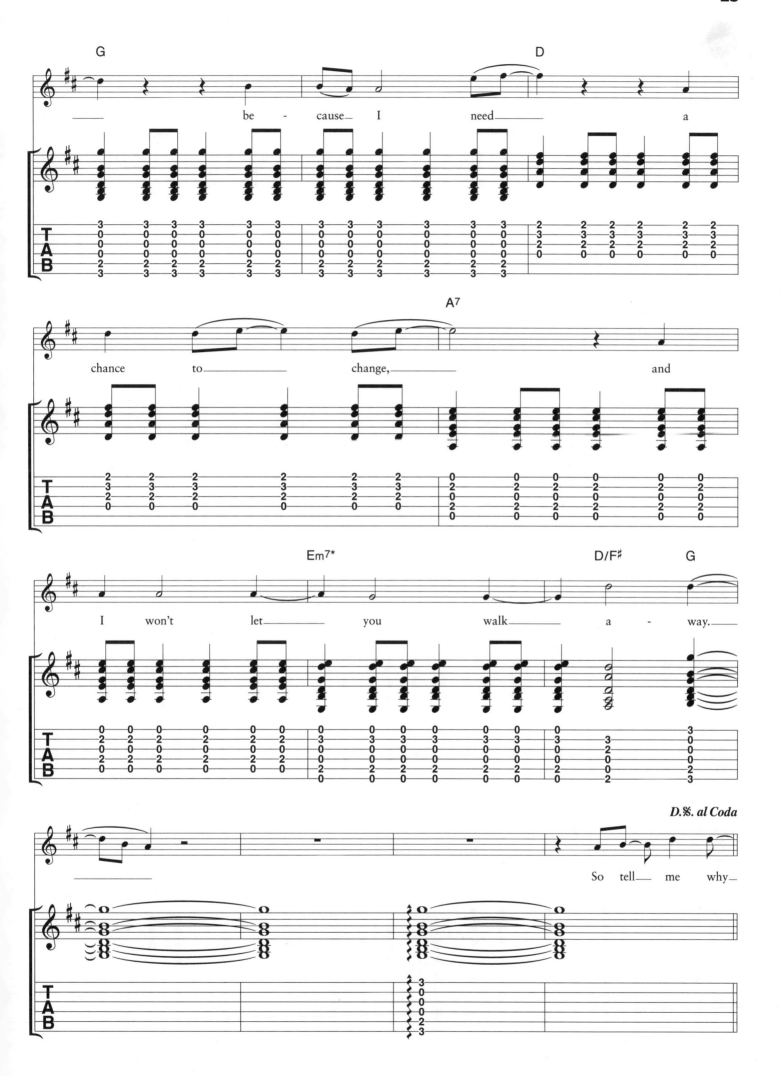

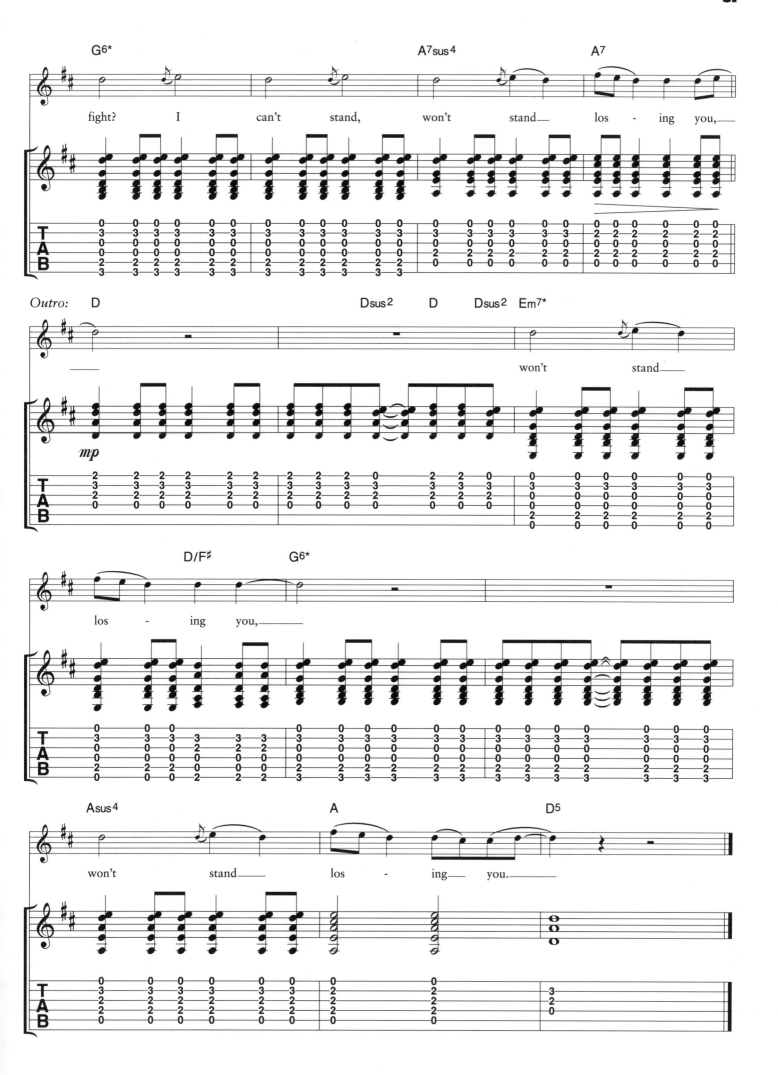

Year 3000

**Words and Music by James Bourne, Mathew Sargeant,
Charlie Simpson and Steve Robson**

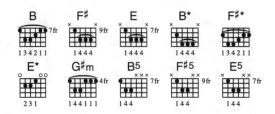

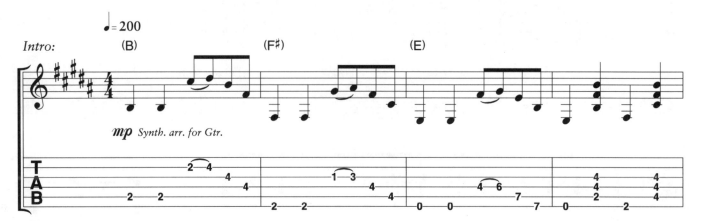

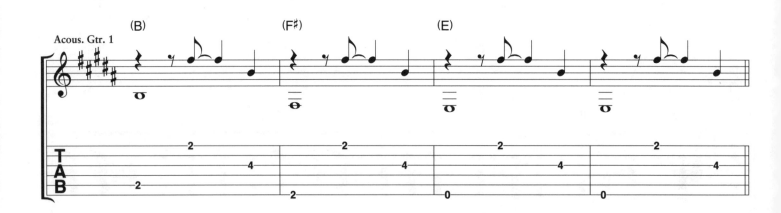

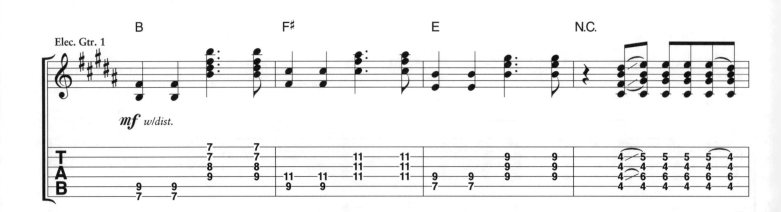

Verse:

1. One day when I came home at lunch-time, I heard a fun-ny noise.
(2.) took me to the fu - ture in the flux thing and I saw ev -'ry-thing.

Went out to the back yard to find—— out if it was one of those row-dy boys.
Boy bands, and an - oth-er one, and an - oth-er one, and an - oth-er one.

Stood there was my neigh-bour called Pe - ter, and a flux ca - pa-ci-tor.
Tri - ple breast-ed wo - men swim a -round town to-tal-ly na - ked!

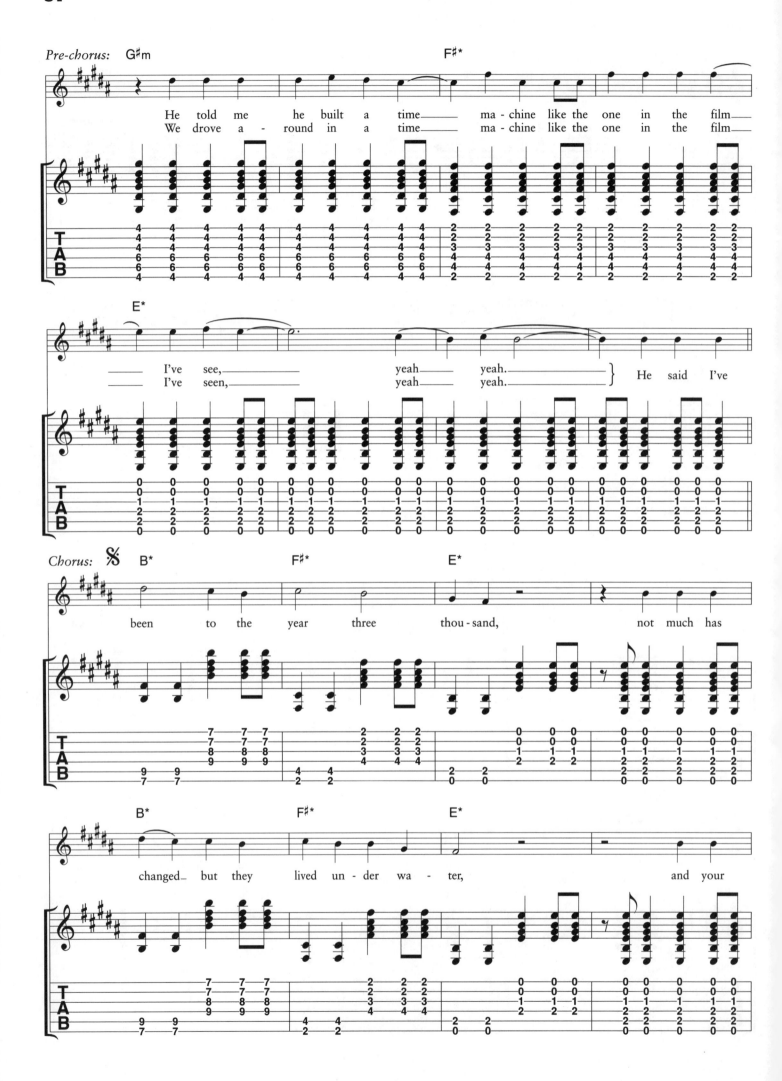

38

Psycho Girl

Words and Music by James Bourne and Steve Robson

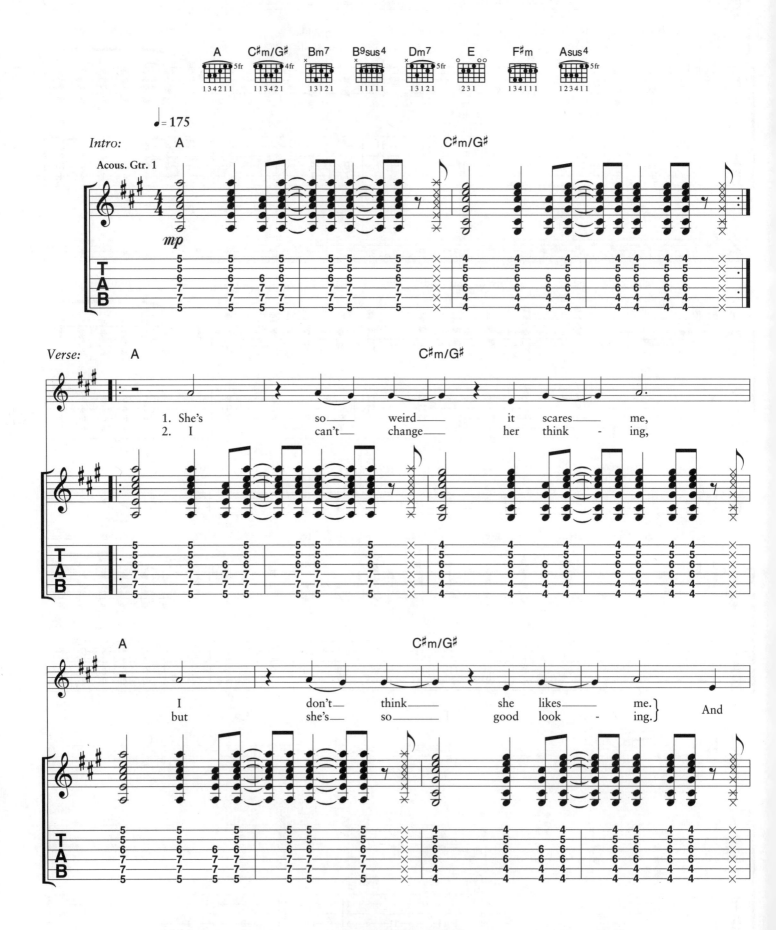

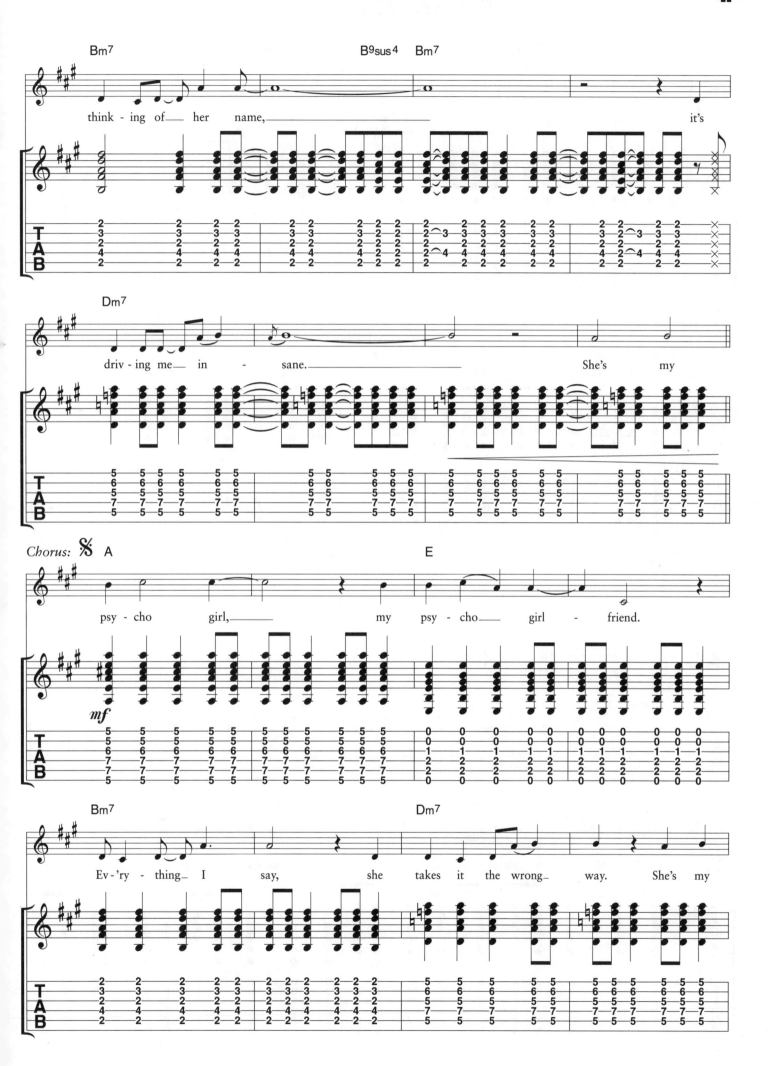

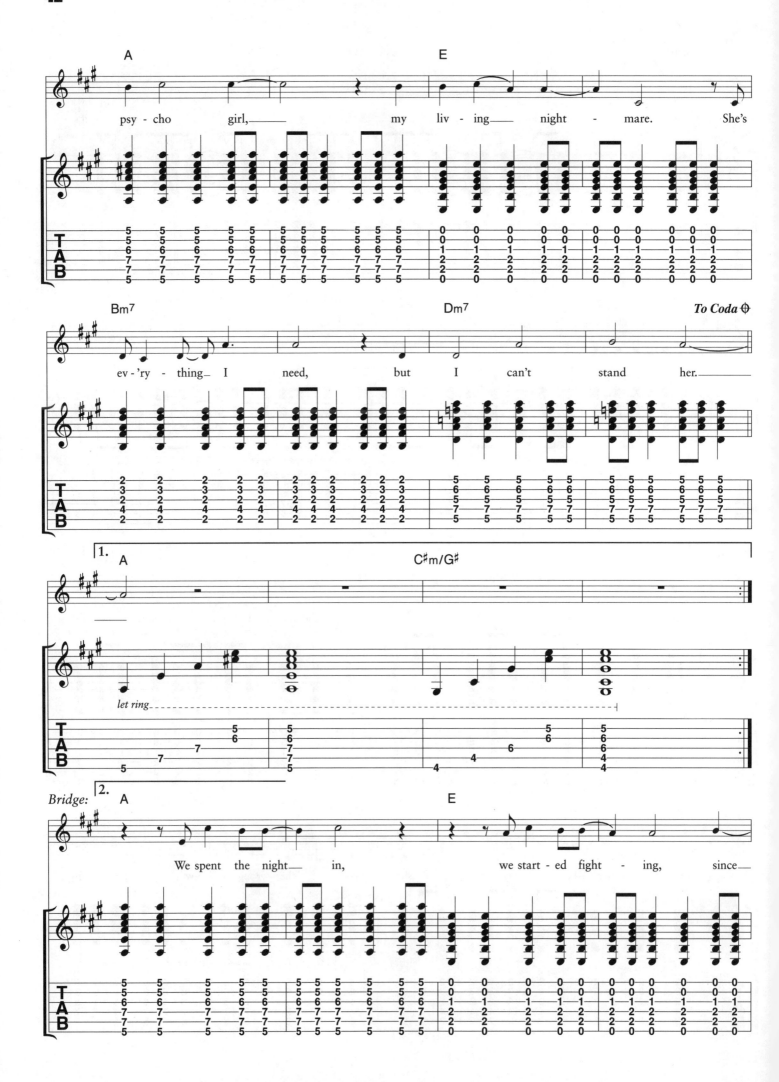

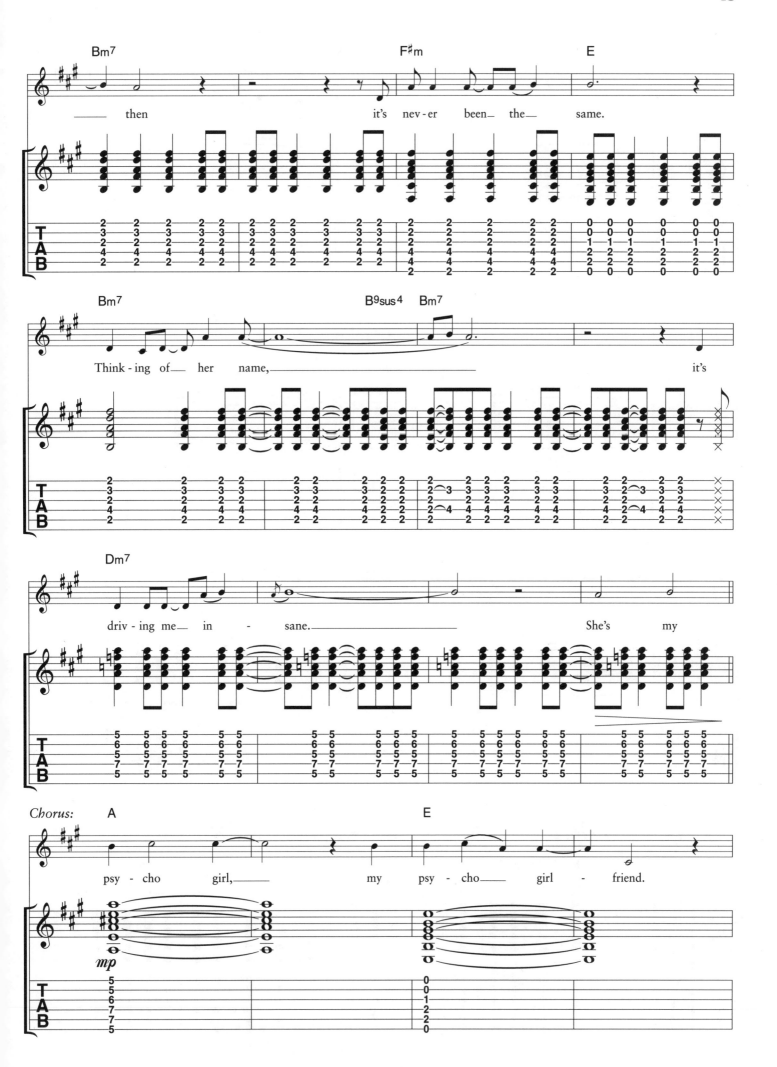

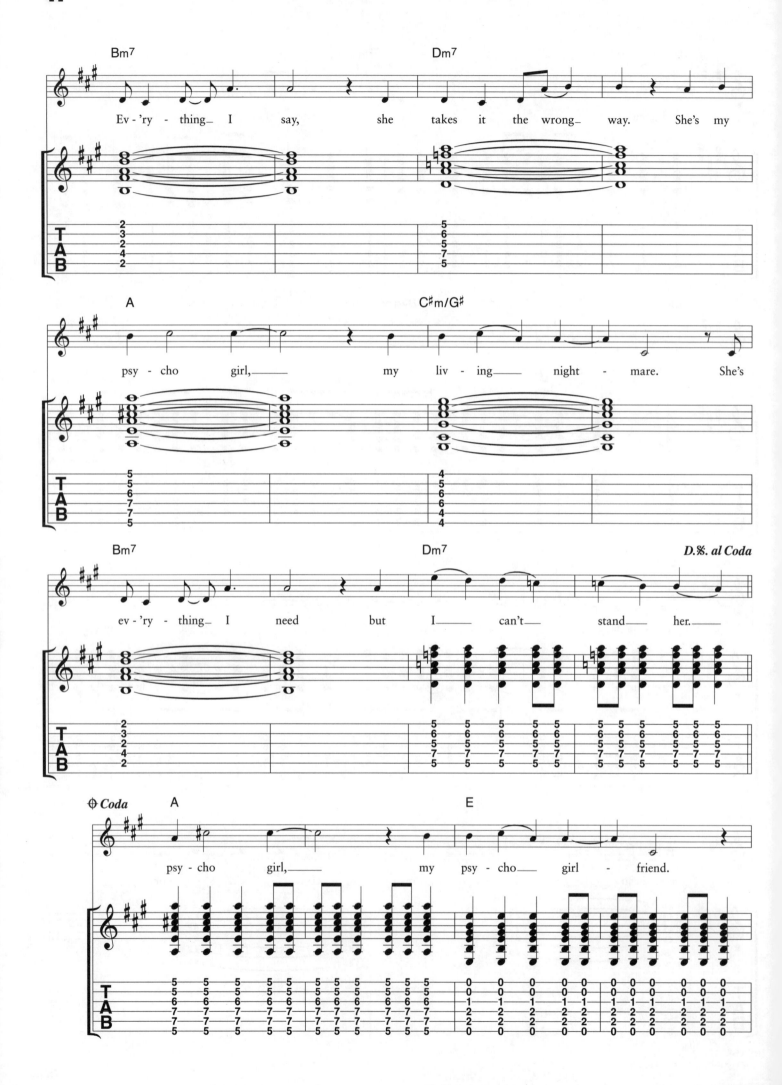

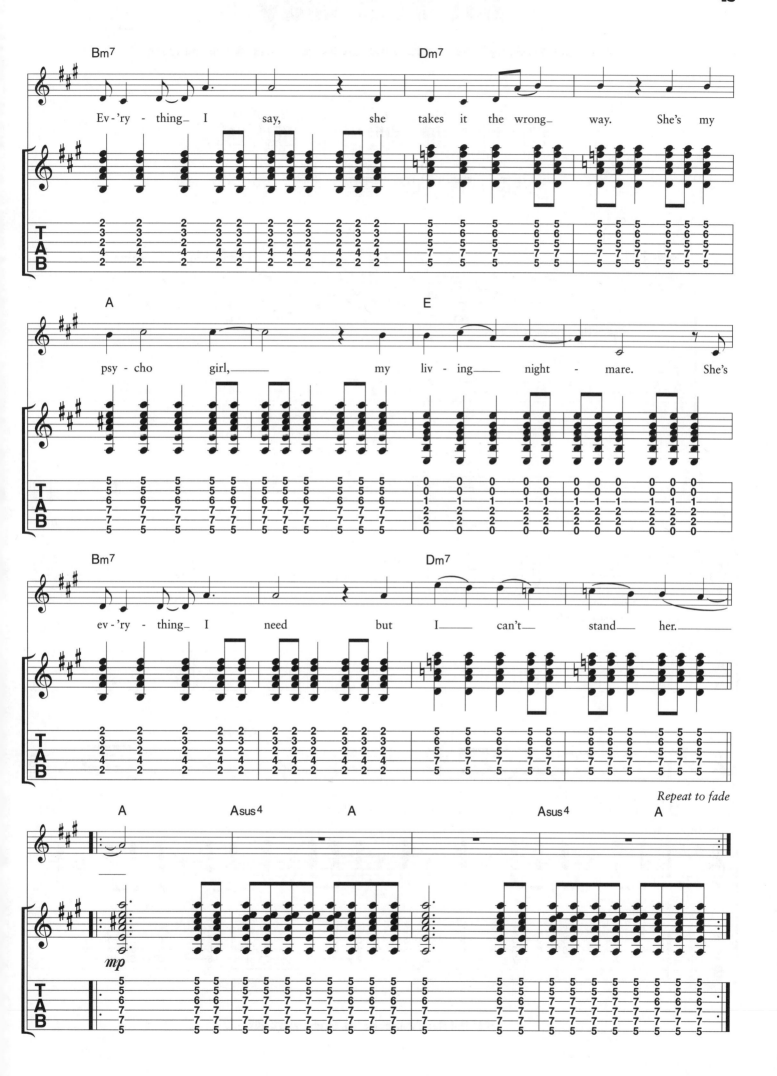

All The Way

Words and Music by James Bourne, Mathew Sargeant and Charlie Simpson

Sleeping With The Light On

Words and Music by James Bourne and Mathew Sargeant

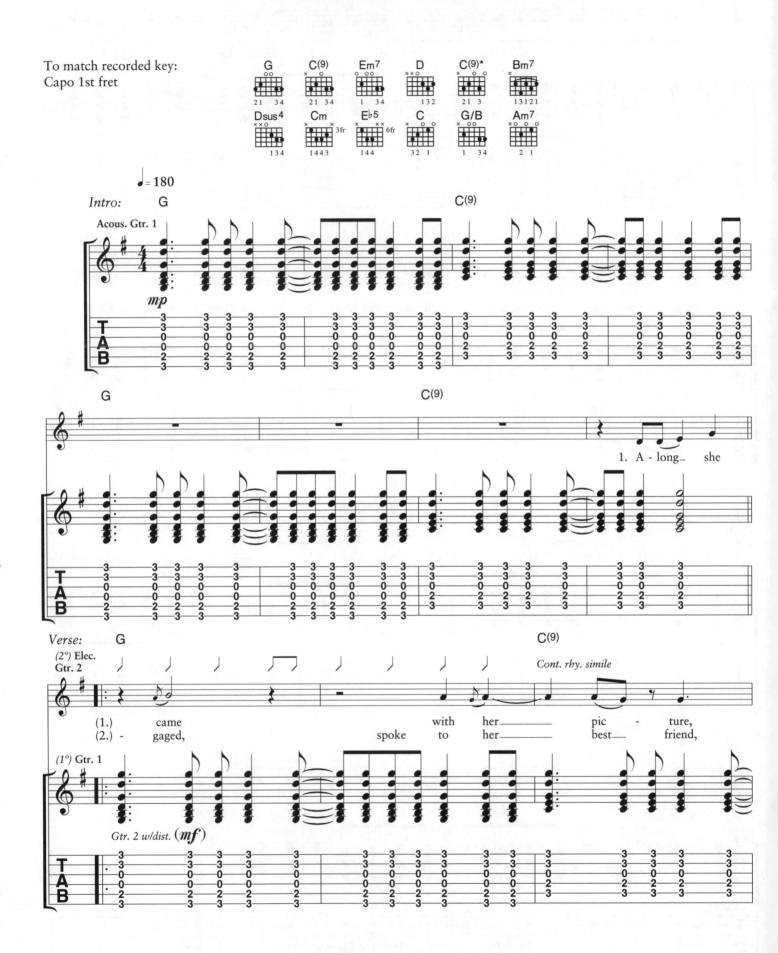

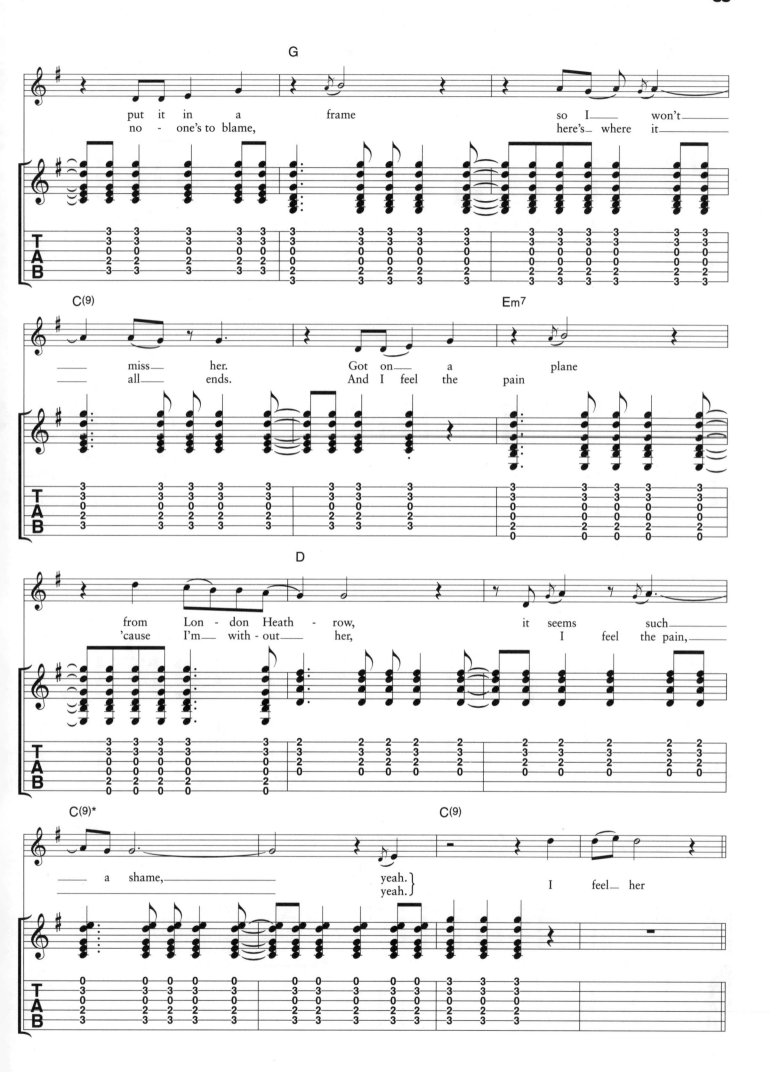

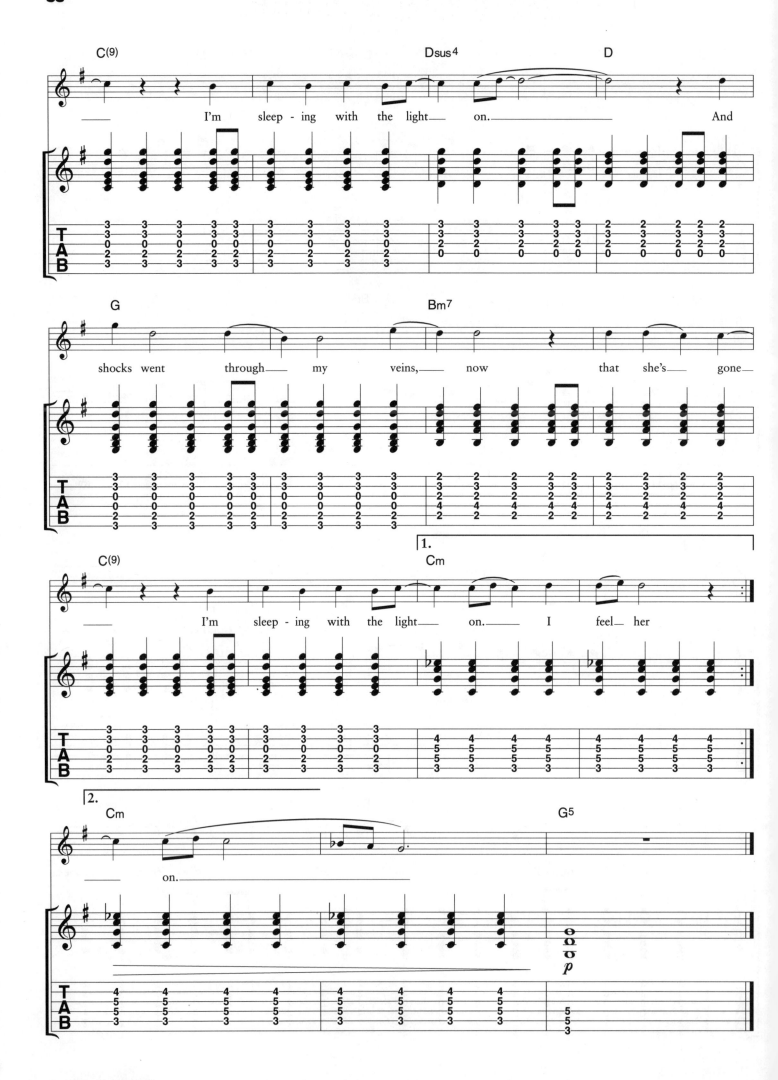

Dawson's Geek

Words and Music by James Bourne, Mathew Sargeant and Charlie Simpson

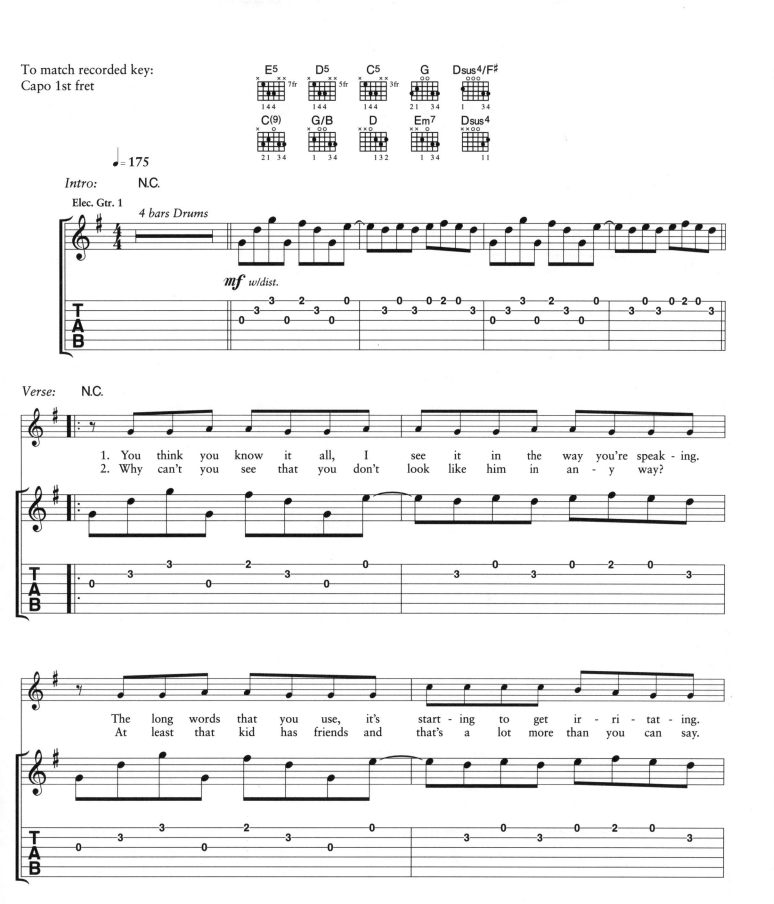

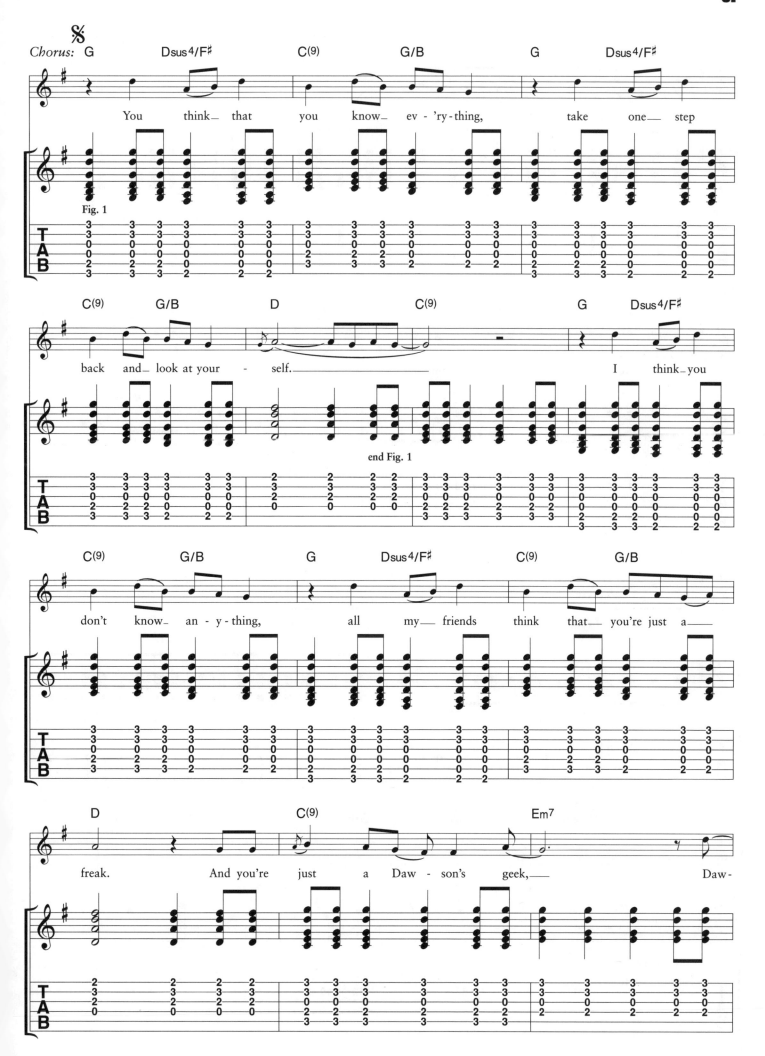

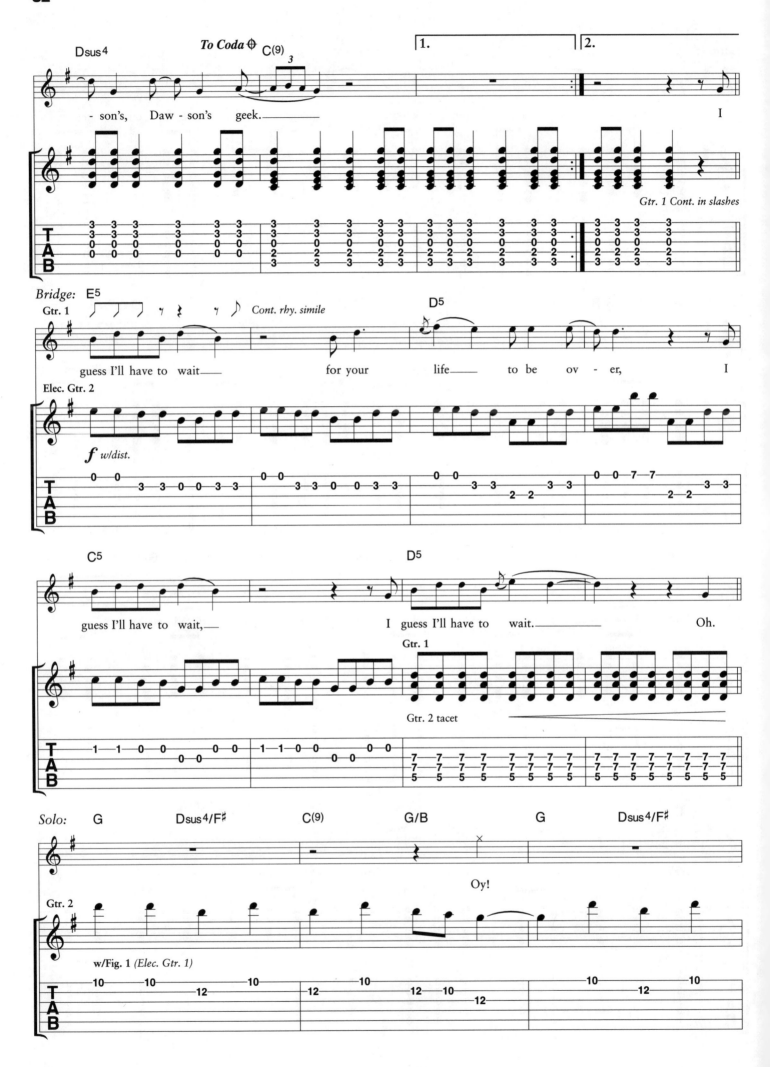

When Day Turns Into Night

Words and Music by James Bourne, Mathew Sargeant, Charlie Simpson, John McLaughlin and Steve Robson

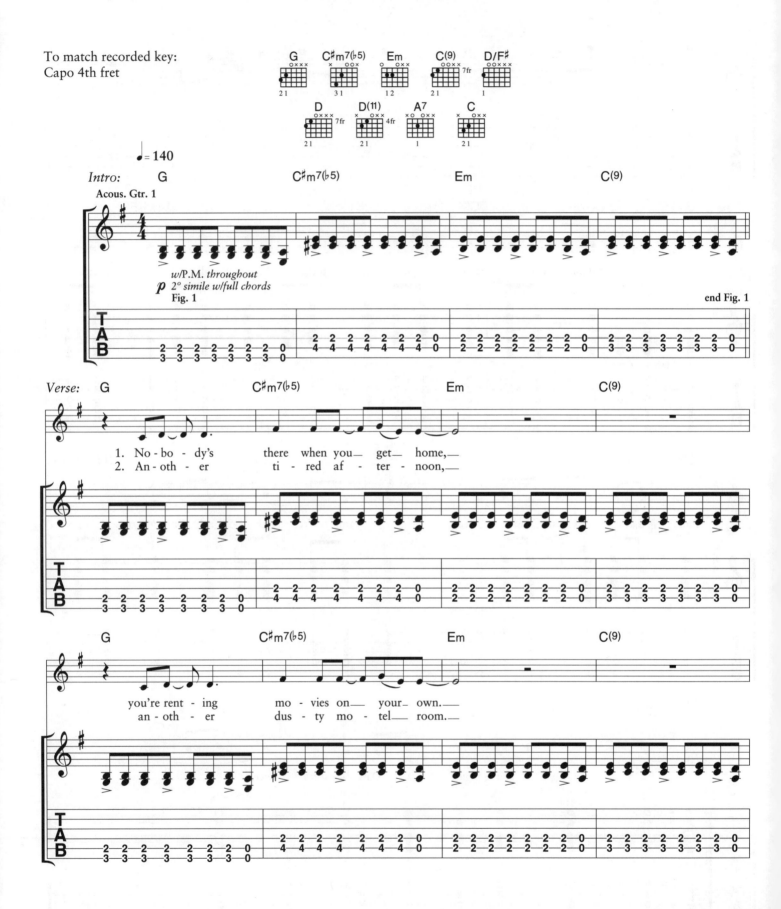

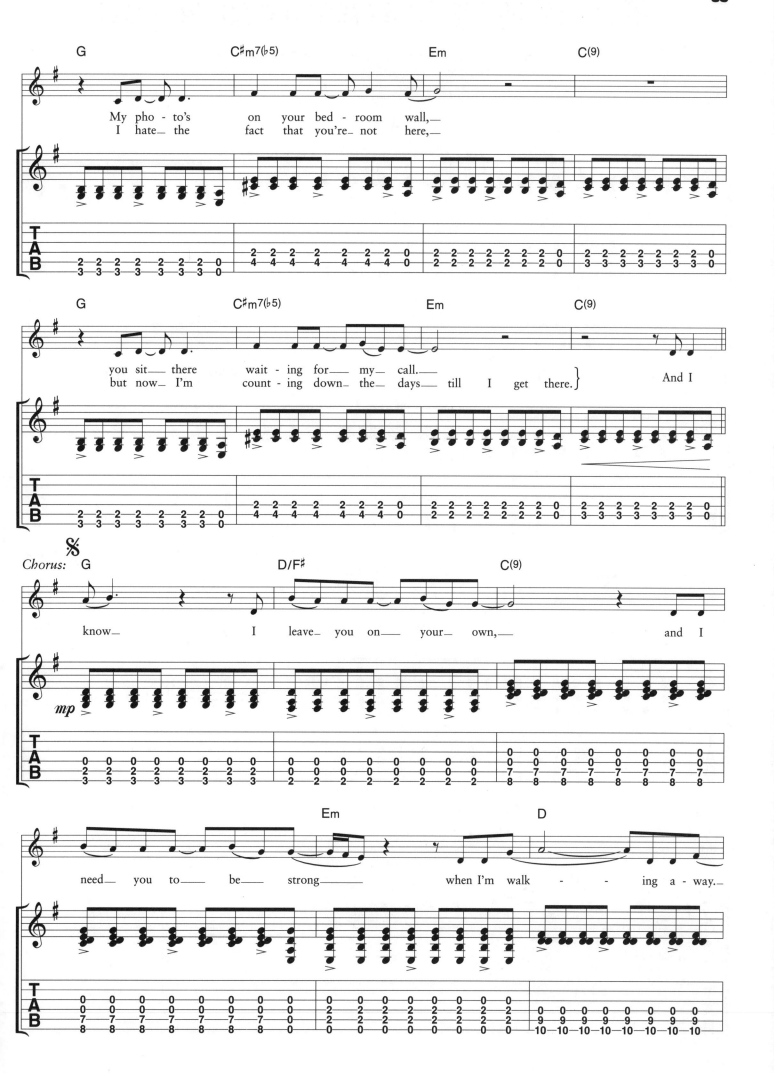

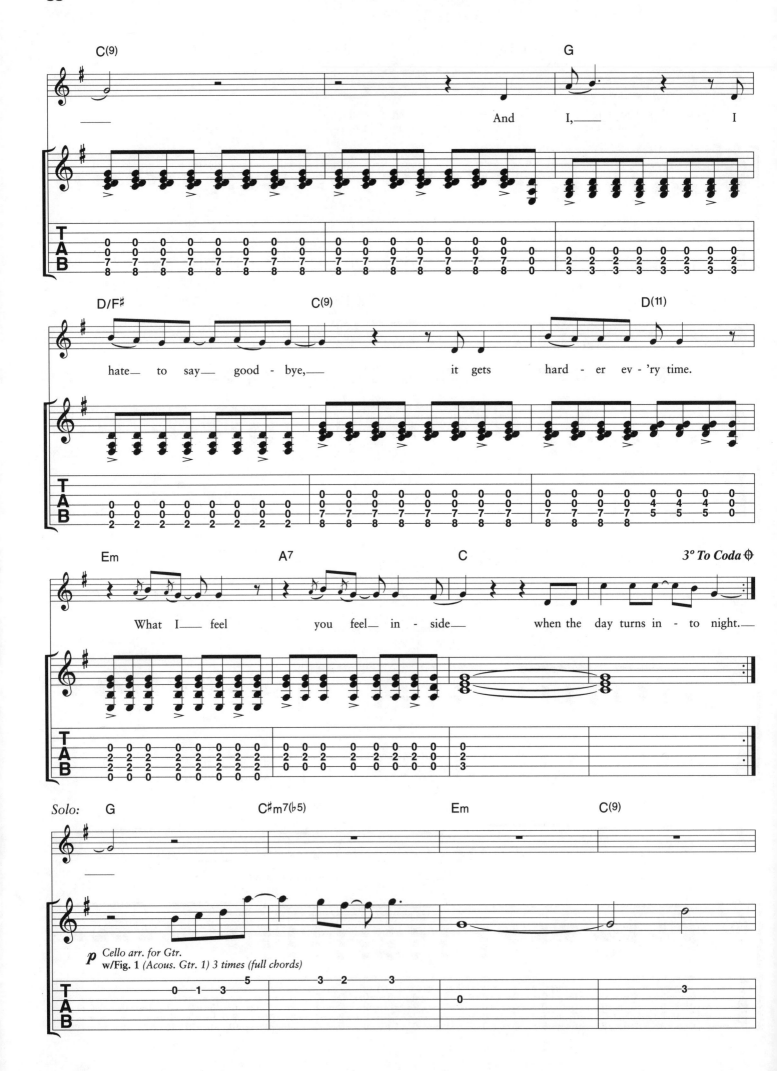

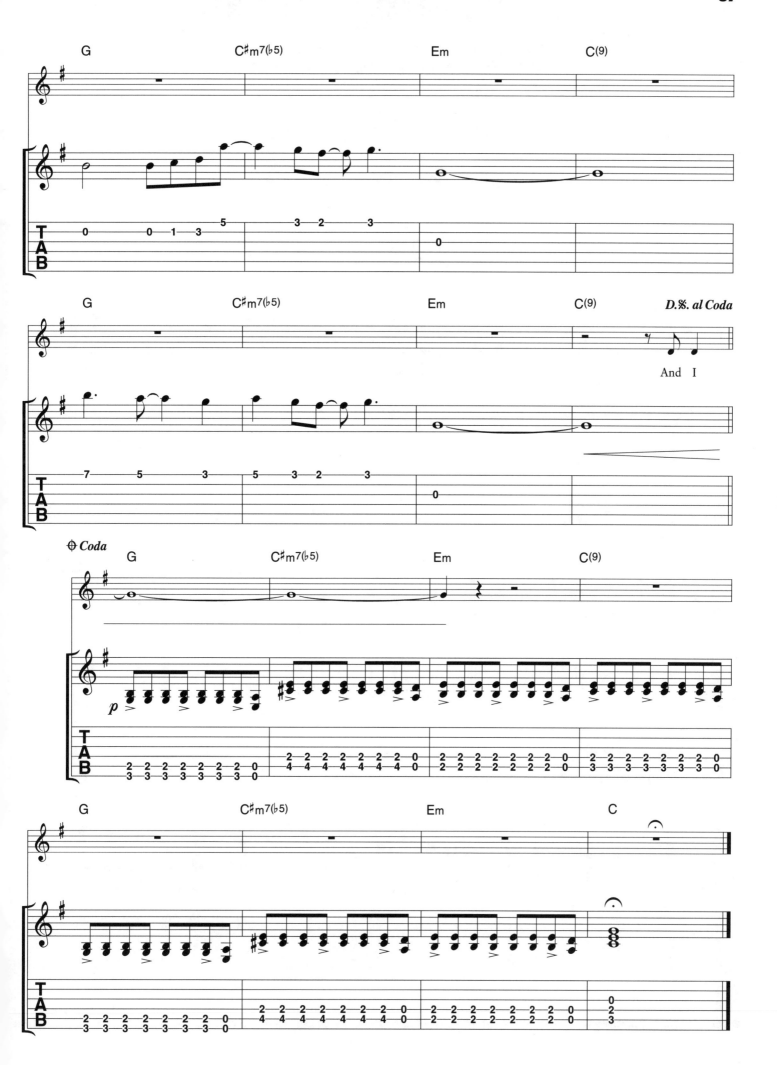

Everything I Knew

Words and Music by James Bourne, Mathew Sargeant, Charlie Simpson, John McLaughlin and Steve Robson

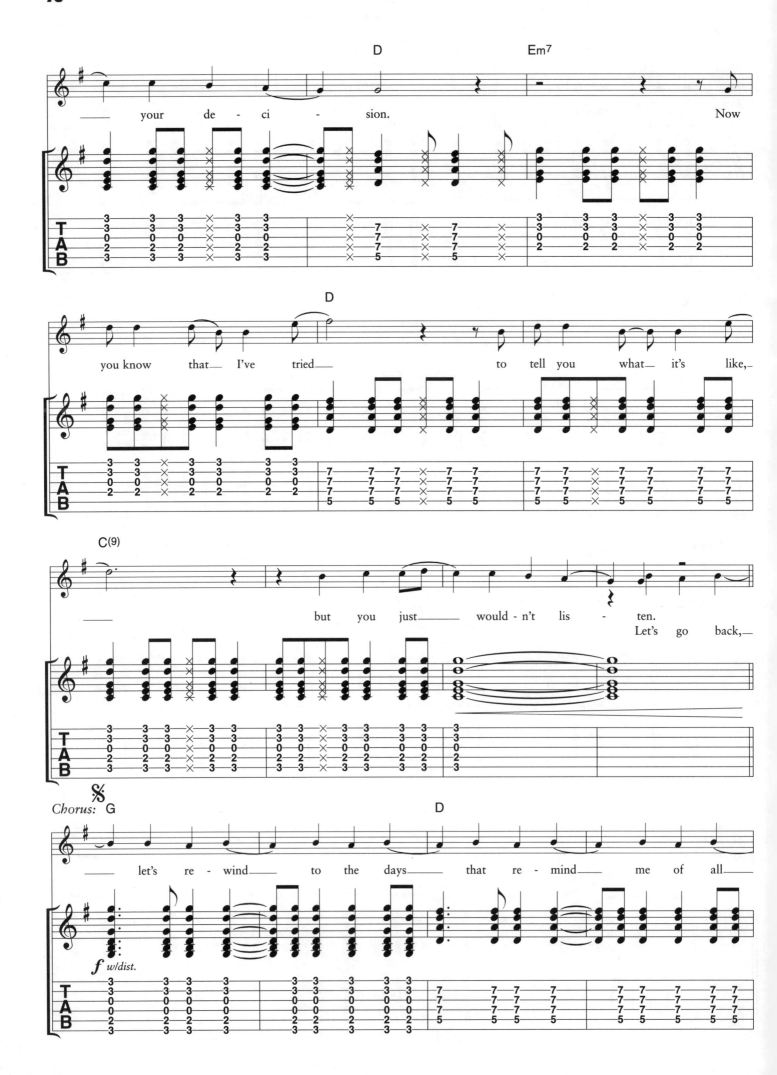

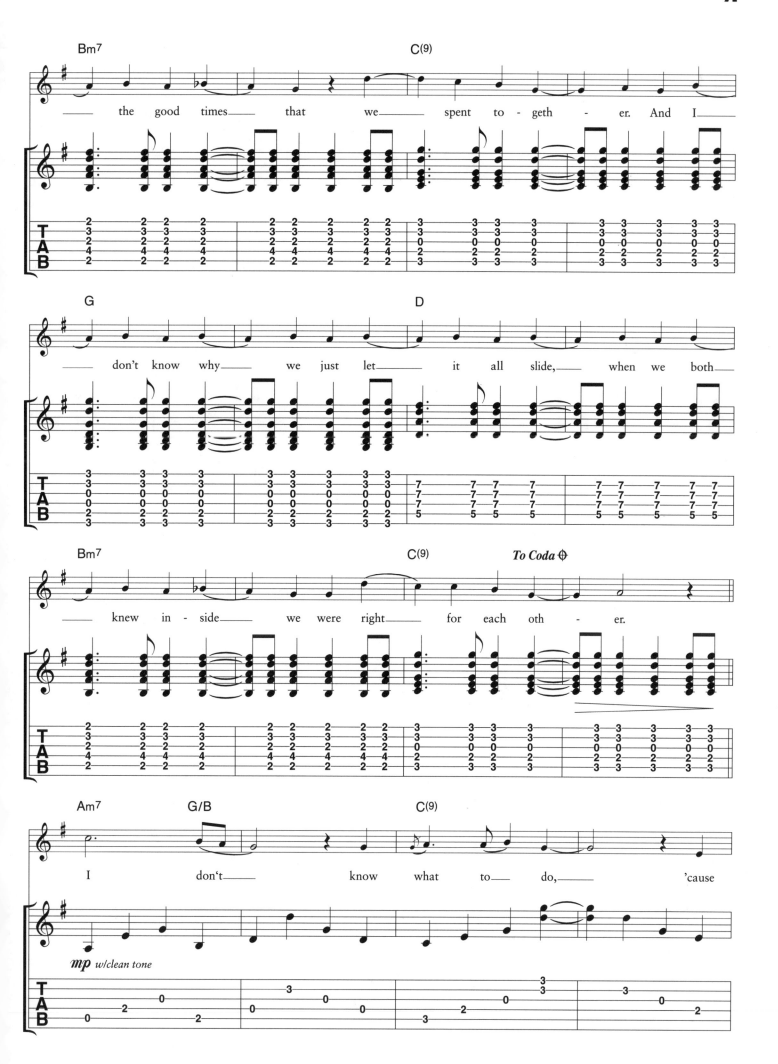

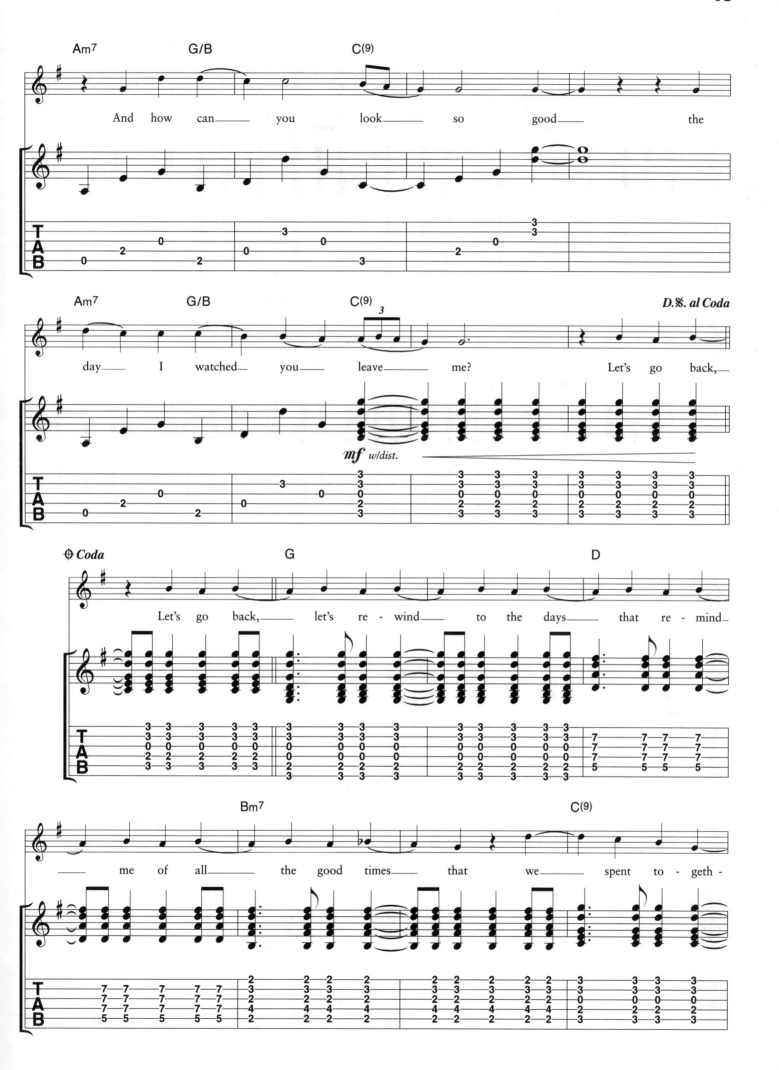

Without You

Words and Music by Charlie Simpson and Steve Robson

Verse 3:
How can I let you leave this way?
Without you I'm not at all
And I see things now, all those memories
Just to see you again.

Loser Kid

Words and Music by James Bourne, Mathew Sargeant and Charlie Simpson

GUITAR TAB GLOSSARY**

TABLATURE EXPLANATION

READING TABLATURE: Tablature illustrates the six strings of the guitar. Notes and chords are indicated by the placement of fret numbers on a given string(s).

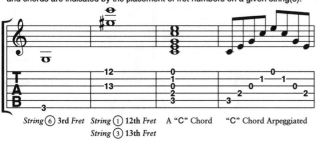

String ⑥ *3rd Fret*   *String* ① *12th Fret*   A "C" Chord   "C" Chord Arpeggiated
String ③ *13th Fret*

BENDING NOTES

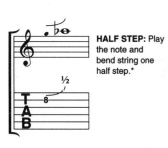

HALF STEP: Play the note and bend string one half step.*

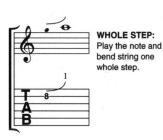

WHOLE STEP: Play the note and bend string one whole step.

WHOLE STEP AND A HALF: Play the note and bend string a whole step and a half.

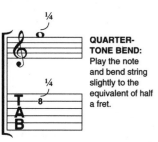

QUARTER-TONE BEND: Play the note and bend string slightly to the equivalent of half a fret.

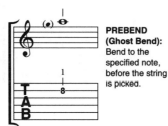

PREBEND (Ghost Bend): Bend to the specified note, before the string is picked.

PREBEND AND RELEASE: Bend the string, play it, then release to the original note.

REVERSE BEND: Play the already-bent string, then immediately drop it down to the fretted note.

BEND AND RELEASE: Play the note and gradually bend to the next pitch, then release to the original note. Only the first note is attacked.

*A half step is the smallest interval in Western music; it is equal to one fret. A whole step equals two frets.

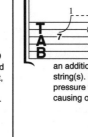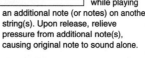

UNISON BEND: Play both notes and immediately bend the lower note to the same pitch as the higher note.

DOUBLE NOTE BEND: Play both notes and immediately bend both strings simultaneously.

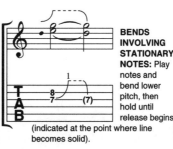

BENDS INVOLVING MORE THAN ONE STRING: Play the note and bend string while playing an additional note (or notes) on another string(s). Upon release, relieve pressure from additional note(s), causing original note to sound alone.

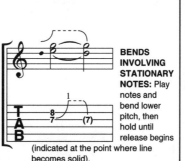

BENDS INVOLVING STATIONARY NOTES: Play notes and bend lower pitch, then hold until release begins (indicated at the point where line becomes solid).

TREMOLO BAR

trem. bar

SPECIFIED INTERVAL: The pitch of a note or chord is lowered to a specified interval and then may or may not return to the original pitch. The activity of the tremolo bar is graphically represented by peaks and valleys.

UN-SPECIFIED INTERVAL: The pitch of a note or a chord is lowered to an unspecified interval.

HARMONICS

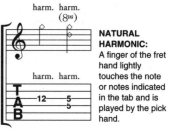

harm. harm.
(8va)

harm. harm.

NATURAL HARMONIC: A finger of the fret hand lightly touches the note or notes indicated in the tab and is played by the pick hand.

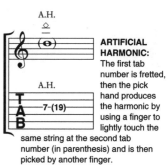

A.H.

ARTIFICIAL HARMONIC: The first tab number is fretted, then the pick hand produces the harmonic by using a finger to lightly touch the same string at the second tab number (in parenthesis) and is then picked by another finger.

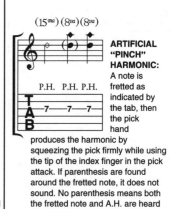

(15ma) (8va) (8va)

P.H. P.H. P.H.

ARTIFICIAL "PINCH" HARMONIC: A note is fretted as indicated by the tab, then the pick hand produces the harmonic by squeezing the pick firmly while using the tip of the index finger in the pick attack. If parenthesis are found around the fretted note, it does not sound. No parenthesis means both the fretted note and A.H. are heard simultaneously.

**By Kenn Chipkin and Aaron Stang

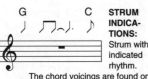

88

RHYTHM SLASHES

G   **C**

STRUM INDICATIONS: Strum with indicated rhythm.

The chord voicings are found on the first page of the transcription underneath the song title.

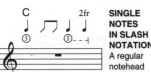

C   **2fr**

SINGLE NOTES IN SLASH NOTATION: A regular notehead indicates a single note. The circled number below the note indicates which string of the chord to strike. If the note is not in the chord, the fret number will be indicated above the note(s).

ARTICULATIONS

HAMMER ON: Play lower note, then "hammer on" to higher note with another finger. Only the first note is attacked.

LEFT HAND HAMMER: Hammer on the first note played on each string with the left hand.

PULL OFF: Play higher note, then "pull off" to lower note with another finger. Only the first note is attacked.

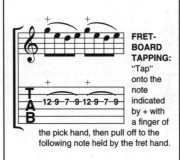

FRET-BOARD TAPPING: "Tap" onto the note indicated by + with a finger of the pick hand, then pull off to the following note held by the fret hand.

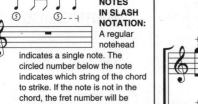

TAP SLIDE: Same as fretboard tapping, but the tapped note is slid randomly up the fretboard, then pulled off to the following note.

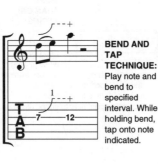

BEND AND TAP TECHNIQUE: Play note and bend to specified interval. While holding bend, tap onto note indicated.

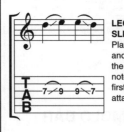

LEGATO SLIDE: Play note and slide to the following note. (Only first note is attacked).

LONG GLISSAN-DO: Play note and slide in specified direction for the full value of the note.

SHORT GLISSAN-DO: Play note for its full value and slide in specified direction at the last possible moment.

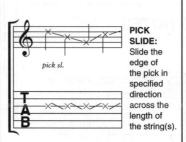

PICK SLIDE: Slide the edge of the pick in specified direction across the length of the string(s).

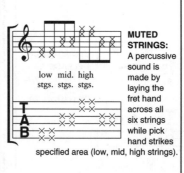

MUTED STRINGS: A percussive sound is made by laying the fret hand across all six strings while pick hand strikes specified area (low, mid, high strings).

PALM MUTE: The note or notes are muted by the palm of the pick hand by lightly touching the string(s) near the bridge.

TREMOLO PICKING: The note or notes are picked as fast as possible.

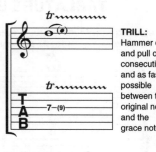

TRILL: Hammer on and pull off consecutively and as fast as possible between the original note and the grace note.

ACCENT: Notes or chords are to be played with added emphasis.

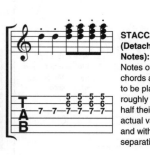

STACCATO (Detached Notes): Notes or chords are to be played roughly half their actual value and with separation.

DOWN STROKES AND UPSTROKES: Notes or chords are to be played with either a downstroke or upstroke of the pick.

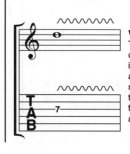

VIBRATO: The pitch of a note is varied by a rapid shaking of the fret hand finger, wrist, and forearm.